KU-556-979

9112000431982

Fact Finders®

→HOW LONG DO STARS LAST?

BY EMILY HUDD

raintree
a Capstone company — publishers for children

Raintree is an imprint of Capstone Global Library Limited, a company incorporated in England and Wales having its registered office at 264 Banbury Road, Oxford, OX2 7DY – Registered company number: 6695582

www.raintree.co.uk
myorders@raintree.co.uk

Text © Capstone Global Library Limited 2020
The moral rights of the proprietor have been asserted.

All rights reserved. No part of this publication may be reproduced in any form or by any means (including photocopying or storing it in any medium by electronic means and whether or not transiently or incidentally to some other use of this publication) without the written permission of the copyright owner, except in accordance with the provisions of the Copyright, Designs and Patents Act 1988 or under the terms of a licence issued by the Copyright Licensing Agency, Barnard's Inn, 86 Fetter Lane, London, EC4A 1EN (www.cla.co.uk). Applications for the copyright owner's written permission should be addressed to the publisher.

Edited by Marie Pearson
Designed by Dan Peluso
Original illustrations © Capstone Global Library Limited 2020
Production by Dan Peluso
Originated by Capstone Global Library Ltd
Printed and bound in India

978 1 4747 8887 8 (hardback)
978 1 4747 8892 2 (paperback)

British Library Cataloguing in Publication Data
A full catalogue record for this book is available from the British Library.

Acknowledgements
We would like to thank the following for permission to reproduce photographs: iStockphoto: Pitris, cover (sun); NASA: ESA, 18, ESA/GSFC, 27, 29 (supernova), ESA/Hubble/GSFC, cover (stars), Goddard/SDO, 14, 29 (main sequence), Hubble Heritage Team/GSFC, 24, 29 (planetary nebula), JPL-Caltech, 23, 29 (white dwarf), 29 (neutron star), 29 (black hole), JPL-Caltech/ESA, the Hubble Heritage Team STScI/AURA and IPHAS, 8, 29 (protostar), JPL-Caltech/STScI, 7, 29 (nebula); Science Source: Davide De Martin, 17, 29 (red giant), John Chumack, 20, Mark Garlick, 10–11, Mark Garlick, 29 (black dwarf); Shutterstock Images: Pozdeyev Vitaly, 13, Yuriy Kulik, 5. Design elements: Red Line Editorial.

Every effort has been made to contact copyright holders of material reproduced in this book. Any omissions will be rectified in subsequent printings if notice is given to the publisher.

All the internet addresses (URLs) given in this book were valid at the time of going to press. However, due to the dynamic nature of the internet, some addresses may have changed, or sites may have changed or ceased to exist since publication. While the author and publisher regret any inconvenience this may cause readers, no responsibility for any such changes can be accepted by either the author or the publisher.

CONTENTS

STARGAZING

It is winter. A girl and her family are bundled up. They are looking at constellations. A constellation is a group of stars that ancient observers thought looked like animals, people and other things. These people named the shapes. The girl's dad points out Orion. Orion is a hunter in Greek legends. He is a strong warrior holding a sword. In the Orion constellation, three stars in the middle make Orion's belt. The star on Orion's leg is the seventh-brightest star in the sky.

The girl notices some stars are red. Others are blue or white. Stars with different colours are different temperatures. Stars have life cycles that can last for billions of years!

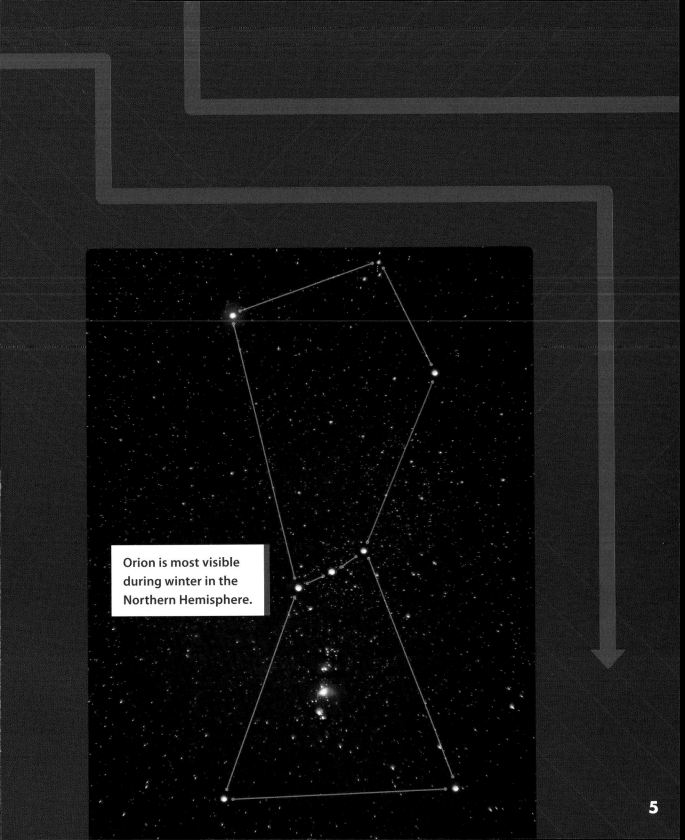

Orion is most visible during winter in the Northern Hemisphere.

CHAPTER ONE

HEATING UP

People can see some large objects such as stars and planets from Earth. What they don't see is what lies between the objects. Outer space is not empty. Dust and gas float through space. Nebulas are clouds of gas and dust. Stars are born in nebulas. **Gravity** pulls gases and dust together. This forms a clump of **dense** gas called a protostar. Protostars are not yet stars. This is the first stage of the star life cycle. The clump grows, and pressure on the centre of the clump increases. This pressure makes the centre very hot. This centre is called the core.

gravity force that pulls objects with mass together; gravity pulls objects down towards the centre of Earth

dense when the matter that makes up an object is packed tightly together

Nebulas come in many colours and patterns.

A protostar grows in a cluster of gas and dust called the Tadpole.

Gravity continues to pull dust and gas, including **hydrogen**, into a ring around the protostar. As gas falls onto the protostar, the protostar spins. The core gets hotter. The star begins to glow. It spins faster as it gathers **matter**.

Big protostars grow faster than small stars. They spin quickly and pull in lots of gas and dust at faster speeds. Big protostars can form in 1 million years. Smaller protostars take longer to form. They spin and grow more slowly. It can take them more than 100 million years to form.

FACT Astronomy is the field of science that studies stars and outer space.

hydrogen natural gas that is found on Earth in the air

matter any substances that make up objects or living things on Earth and outer space

The ring of dust and gas around a protostar forms outer layers around the core. The layers are joined to the core by gravity. Gravity pulls gas into the core.

FACT

The Sun is a slightly larger than average star. It formed in about 50 million years.

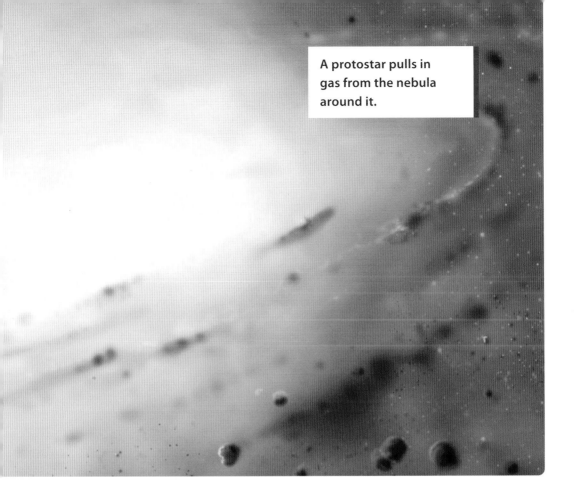

A protostar pulls in gas from the nebula around it.

The layers put more pressure on the core. The core gets even hotter.

Growing is an important part of a star's life cycle. A star's **mass** determines how long it will live and how it will die.

mass amount of matter in something

CHAPTER TWO

BRIGHT
STAR

When a protostar's core reaches 8 million degrees Celsius (15 million degrees Fahrenheit), it becomes a star. In this second stage of life, the star is called a main sequence star. It shines brightly because of the core's high temperature and **density**. Hydrogen fuels the core. There is more hydrogen in the universe than any other energy source. Gravity and heat cause hydrogen to **fuse**. This turns hydrogen into the gas helium. The process produces lots of light.

FACT
The process of hydrogen turning into helium in the core of a star is called nuclear fusion.

density measure of the weight of an object compared to its size
fuse combine multiple things together

People can see some stars from Earth. But there are many more stars that are too far away to be seen with the naked eye.

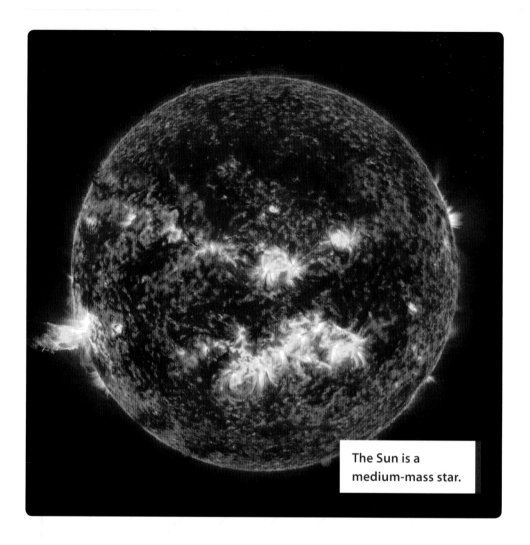

The Sun is a medium-mass star.

The light shines brightly. People can see some stars from Earth.

FACT

Ninety per cent of all stars are in the main sequence stage. The Sun is a main sequence star.

Stars spend 90 per cent of their lives as main sequence stars. This stage is the longest in the star's life cycle. It can last for millions or billions of years.

Stars with a large mass live shorter lives than lower mass stars. They use up hydrogen quickly. Small stars live longer because they use energy more slowly. They can live for billions of years.

BRIGHTEST STAR IN THE SKY

Sirius, also called the dog star, is the brightest star in the night sky. It is part of the Canis Major constellation, which is shaped like a dog. Sirius is a main sequence star. It shines a blue-white colour. It is the brightest star people can see in the night sky because it is very close to Earth. It is 8.6 **light years** away.

light year distance light travels in one year; it is equal to 9.5 trillion kilometres (5.9 trillion miles)

CHAPTER THREE

RED GIANT

Eventually, all the hydrogen in the star's core gets used up. It has been turned into helium. The core shrinks, but the outer layers expand. The lower layers are so hot that they push the outer layers away. The star grows wider.

This is the third stage of the star. It is a red giant. It is named after the way it looks. It is larger than before. It glows red. This is because the temperature in the outer layers is lower than that in the core. The outer layers form a bright shell of gas around the central star.

FACT

Stars expand to more than 400 times their original size as red giants.

Betelgeuse is a red giant star. It is in the constellation Orion.

The star cools. It is a red giant. It can swallow matter or planets nearby as it swells.

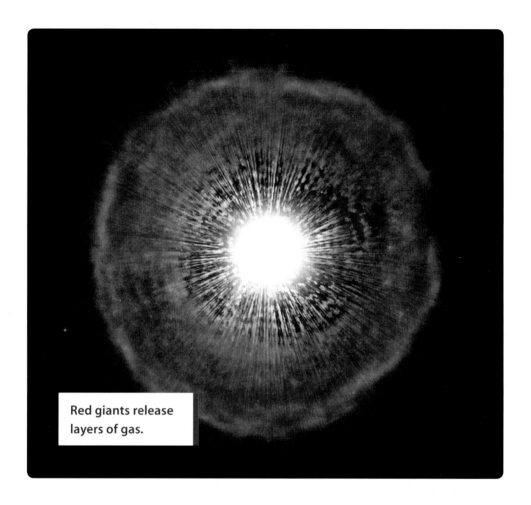

Red giants release layers of gas.

The Sun will engulf Mercury and Venus as a red giant. It may even reach as far as Earth. But this will not happen soon. The Sun will not become a red giant for another 5 billion years.

STAR RANKINGS

Stars are classified by mass and temperature. There are seven different groups. Each group is represented by a letter. Group M includes the coolest stars. Then, groups K, G, F, A and B get hotter. Group O contains the largest and hottest stars. Additionally, stars in each group can be ranked zero to nine for finer temperature divisions. Zero is the hottest temperature. The Sun's classification is G2.

During the red giant stage, the star continues to give off energy. There is no more hydrogen in its core. It uses hydrogen from its outer layers instead. All the hydrogen in the layers turns into helium.

Once all the hydrogen in the core is changed to helium, the star needs a new energy source. The star's core gets hotter. It becomes hot enough to burn helium as fuel. It starts with the helium in the core. The helium turns to **carbon**.

carbon natural substance that is found on Earth in rocks and all living things

A star's temperature determines its colour. A star changes colours throughout its life. Usually it starts as yellow and white. Most main sequence stars range from red for the lowest mass stars to yellow to white to blue for the most massive. When stars cool, they turn to orange or red.

Arcturus is a red giant in the constellation Boötes.

STAR TEMPERATURES AND COLOURS

The surface temperature of blue stars is more than 30,000 degrees Celsius (54,000°F). White and yellow stars range from 10,000 to 6,000 degrees Celsius (18,000 to 11,000°F). Red stars are less than 3,000 degrees Celsius (5,000°F).

The red giant stage happens at the end of the star's life. Most stars spend the last 10 per cent of their lives as red giants. The red giant stage is shorter than the main sequence stage because helium burns faster than hydrogen. The star can use up all the helium in a few thousand years. As the helium runs out, the outer layers shrink. All stars evolve in the same way during the red giant stage. What happens next depends on the mass of the star.

CHAPTER FOUR

DWARF OR SUPERNOVA?

A star's life comes to an end after the red giant phase. It has burned all of its fuel. A star's mass determines how it will die. A star with medium or low mass becomes a white **dwarf star**. This includes stars that are the size of the Sun. In the first step, the outer layers of the star become planetary nebulas. They form at the end of the red giant phase. When the red giant shrinks, it casts off its outer layers into space. These are planetary nebulas.

dwarf star star with smaller than usual size and mass

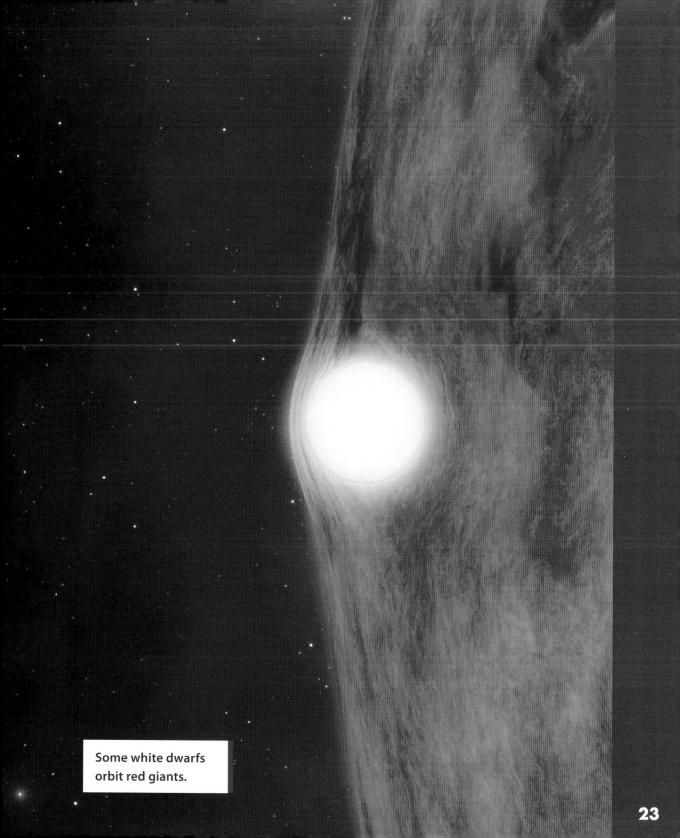

Some white dwarfs
orbit red giants.

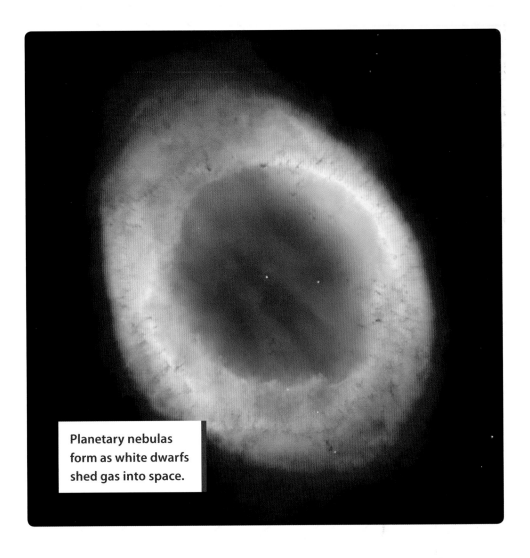

Planetary nebulas
form as white dwarfs
shed gas into space.

Planetary nebulas live short lives compared to stars. For tens of thousands of years, they are scattered in space.

Sometimes they glow because they are absorbing energy from the star they were part of. Planetary nebulas continue the star life cycle.

Eventually, all the star's layers drift into space. Only the core is left. It is very hot and shines brightly. The core is now a white dwarf star. White dwarfs are made of carbon and **oxygen**. They are a similar size to Earth, but very dense. A spoonful of this matter would have about the same mass as Mount Everest. This is the last stage for low-mass stars that scientists have seen.

FACT
The surface of white dwarfs can be more than 100,000 degrees Celsius (180,000°F). They are some of the hottest stars in space.

oxygen gas that is needed for many things on Earth, including breathing and breaking things down

Scientists think there is another stage after white dwarfs. A white dwarf slowly cools and dims. All its energy goes away. It stops shining and turns dark. It is a black dwarf. Scientists think it could take trillions of years for a white dwarf to cool and become a black dwarf. The universe is only 13.8 billion years old. So none have formed yet.

Massive stars take a different path after the red giant stage. They may become **supernovas**. Supernovas are explosions. An explosion happens when a red giant star runs out of fuel.

> **FACT**
> The core temperature of a star just before a supernova is more than 555 million degrees Celsius (100 billion°F).

At the end of the red giant's life, there is no more energy to support the star.

supernova explosion of a star at the end of its life cycle

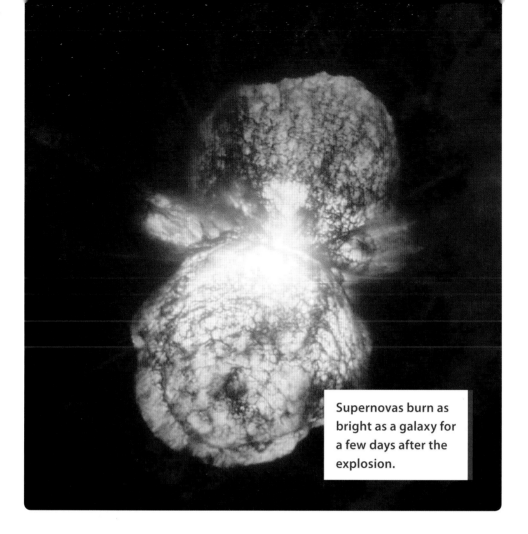

Supernovas burn as bright as a galaxy for a few days after the explosion.

In less than a second, gravity causes the outer layers to cave in. This causes a powerful supernova explosion. Dust and elements are blasted far into space.

The dense core of the supernova is left after the explosion. It will become a **neutron star** if its mass is less than two to three times that of the Sun. This is the last stage for massive stars. The explosion causes the neutron star to spin quickly. It can spin several hundred times per second.

If the star is more than two to three times as massive as the Sun, it becomes a black hole. Black holes are the rarest end for stars. After the explosion, the black hole has strong gravity. The gravity pulls everything towards the black hole. Scientists can't see what is in black holes. Even light is sucked in.

FACT
Neutron stars are more dense than white dwarfs. A neutron star that is only 20 kilometres (12 miles) across could weigh as much as two Suns.

neutron star very dense star that is the result of the collapse of a much larger star

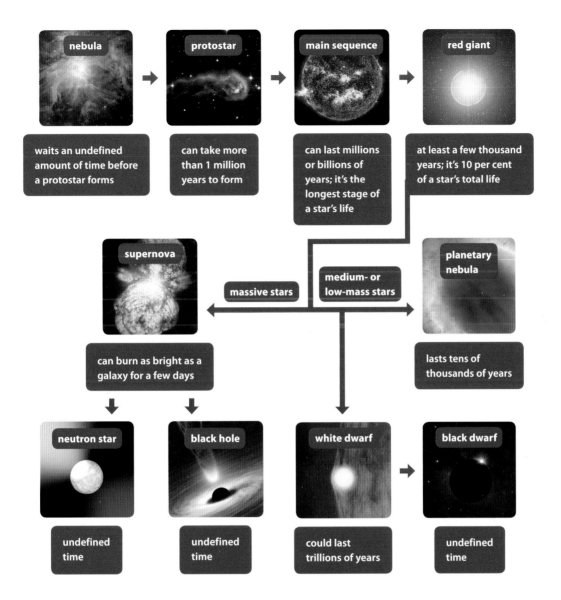

nebula
waits an undefined amount of time before a protostar forms

protostar
can take more than 1 million years to form

main sequence
can last millions or billions of years; it's the longest stage of a star's life

red giant
at least a few thousand years; it's 10 per cent of a star's total life

massive stars

medium- or low-mass stars

supernova
can burn as bright as a galaxy for a few days

planetary nebula
lasts tens of thousands of years

neutron star
undefined time

black hole
undefined time

white dwarf
could last trillions of years

black dwarf
undefined time

Stars have an amazing life cycle. They can last millions or billions of years.

GLOSSARY

carbon natural substance that is found on Earth in rocks and all living things

dense when the matter that makes up an object is packed tightly together

density measure of the weight of an object compared to its size

dwarf star star with smaller than usual size and mass

fuse combine multiple things together

gravity force that pulls objects with mass together; gravity pulls objects down towards the centre of Earth

hydrogen natural gas that is found on Earth in the air

light year distance light travels in one year; it is equal to 9.5 trillion kilometres (5.9 trillion miles)

mass amount of matter in something

matter any substances that make up objects or living things on Earth and outer space

neutron star very dense star that is the result of the collapse of a much larger star

oxygen gas that is needed for many things on Earth, including breathing and breaking things down

supernova explosion of a star at the end of its life cycle

FIND OUT MORE

BOOKS

Knowledge Encyclopedia Space! The Universe as You've Never Seen it Before, DK (DK Children, 2015)

Stars and Galaxies (Astronauts Travel Guides), Isabel Thomas (Raintree, 2013)

What Do We Know About Stars and Galaxies? (Earth, Space and Beyond), John Farndon (Raintree, 2012)

WEBSITES

www.dkfindout.com/uk/space/stars-and-galaxies
Find out more about stars and galaxies.

www.esa.int/kids/en/learn?s509517/s509536
Learn more about the life cycle of stars.

COMPREHENSION QUESTIONS

1. What is the difference between protostars and main sequence stars? Use evidence from the text to support your answer.

2. After the red giant stage, a star can die in different ways. Describe the path a star can take when it dies.

3. The star life cycle can last millions or billions of years. Would you want to live as long as a star? Why?

INDEX